Snailopolis

Thematic Science Unit

Written and Illustrated by
Karen G. Frandsen

Graphic Design by
Chip Dombrowski

Edited by
Patricia Gray
Chip Dombrowski

© 2015
THE CRITICAL THINKING CO.™
www.CriticalThinking.com
Phone: 800-458-4849 • Fax: 541-756-1758
1991 Sherman Ave., Suite 200 • North Bend • OR 97459
ISBN 978-1-60144-773-9

TABLE of CONTENTS

ABOUT THE AUTHOR

Illustrator and writer Karen Frandsen has always been a dreamer — or so say her report cards. It turns out that dreaming was the gift that guided her actions as a mom, teacher, and entrepreneur. Born in North Dakota, Karen moved to California at age 2. She graduated from San Diego State University with a degree in art and a teaching credential.

When the offer was presented, Karen jumped at the opportunity to create a science lab for students in Grades K-6 that incorporated science, art, math, and language arts. She created units in which students explored in a hands-on environment through research, investigation, oral presentation, and collaboration.

While still teaching, Karen opened her company (Karen's Kids Products), hired employees and continued to teach until 1999. Karen now lives in Cardiff-by-the-Sea near her family and friends, and creates characters, curriculum, and products full time.

ABOUT THIS BOOK

Snailopolis is a hands-on unit of study that integrates science, reading, math, language, and art through the hands-on observation of snails. Common Core Standards are applied in each activity and extension activities are included.

Each activity includes a Teacher Page and one or more Student Activity Forms. Teacher Pages include suggested time for lesson, materials for that lesson, and **SAY – DO** guidelines.

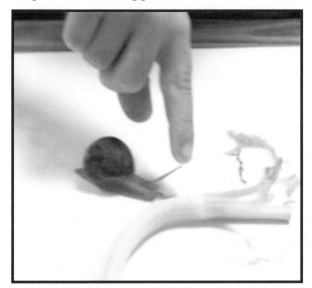

Age Range Adaptable
K through Grade 4. Some activities have separate versions for ■ Grades K-2 and ■ Grades 2-4.

Overview and Purpose
This unit was developed to provide students with opportunities to obtain, evaluate, and communicate information through the hands-on study of snails and their environment. Students participate in science, math, writing (creative and factual), art, and interaction with other students. They predict, observe, research, touch, experiment, and record information.

Objective
Students will describe what a snail looks like, name its parts, identify three or more facts about snails, as well as compare and contrast unique characteristics of snails and humans.

Process Skills
Science process skills form the foundation for the scientific method. Students will observe, communicate, classify, measure, infer, predict as well as investigate, collect data, describe, and evaluate.

Curriculum Integration and Common Core Standards
This integrated unit includes math, science, art, writing, research, oral presentation, and discussion. Common Core Standards are referenced at the end of the unit.

SNAIL FACTS

(Refer to this page throughout *Snailopolis*.)

Snails belong to a group of animals with soft bodies called mollusks. A snail's soft body is protected by a shell. Another name for a snail is *gastropod,* which means "stomach foot," gastro for stomach and pod for foot. These invertebrates (animals with no backbone) are found worldwide in oceans, lakes, rivers, marshes, and moist areas on land.

The snail retreats into its shell and seals the entrance in dry or cold weather to protect its body from drying out. Snails are most active at night (nocturnal) and on cloudy days, rather than during the day (diurnal).

The first thing a newly hatched snail does is look for food. It eats its eggshell and sometimes eggs that have not yet hatched. As the snail grows, its shell grows into a spiral shape. The part of the shell that the baby hatched with becomes the middle of the spiral called the apex.

A snail moves by creeping on its foot, swimming, or floating. The powerful muscles in the foot contract and expand and this creates a ripple that pushes the snail forward. The slimy mucus is produced by a gland in the foot. This mucus leaves shiny tracks on the leaves of plants, concrete, or other surfaces. The mucus hardens when it comes into contact with air. The snail is able to move oversharp objects, even across a razor blade without being injured because the mucus helps to protect its body.

Snails range in size from .02 inches (less than a millimeter) long to over 30 inches long. The largest land snail is the Giant African Snail. It is over 15 inches long and weighs about two pounds.

Snails have two pairs of tentacles on the head. Land snails have a light-sensitive eye spot located on each of the larger tentacles. The smaller pair of tentacles is used for the senses of smell and touch. Snails have no ears so they cannot hear.

Snails have enemies including people, beetles, snakes, toads, turtles, birds, chickens, ducks, and geese.

Some snails are carnivores (meat eaters) and some are herbivores (plant eaters). They have a radula which is a hard plate with many teeth.

The SNAIL FACT OR FICTION CARDS (page 5) include more amazing facts.

Additional information can be found online.
http://molluscs.at/gastropoda/index.html?/gastropoda/morphology/body_construction.html

SNAILOPOLIS MATERIALS LIST

Gather all your materials together before beginning the lessons. Hide the snail community, Snailopolis, until it is time for the first hands-on lesson.

 ## Snails

1 per team of 2 students. Have extras for students who work better alone.

Chances are if you have a garden, you have snails. Check your backyard or local nursery before ordering snails from a science supply company.

Contact your school for the name(s) of biology supply companies they already work with.*

 ## Celery

One bunch should last for the unit.

 ## Small, clear plastic containers with covers and air holes, one per snail

Markets and deli departments are usually eager to donate plastic containers for school projects. Sending a Thank You note is appreciated too. (page 60)

 ## Damp garden soil, dead leaves, and/or pieces of bark

 Consider putting items with √ on desks **prior** to the first lesson. It builds excitement and mystery when the students enter the room.

- √ Small paper nut cups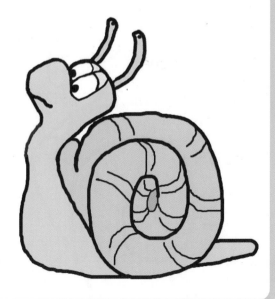
- √ 10-20 small counters
    washers, buttons, pennies
- √ Hand lenses
    magnifying glasses
- √ Pencils
- √ Rulers
- √ Washable paint
    possible colors: red, blue, green, violet
- √ Newspapers for laying on desks

 ## Student Activity Forms

You can staple student activity forms together into a booklet or pass out individual pages with corresponding lesson.

*If you want to receive land snails from a science supply company in a state other than yours, you may be required by the USDA to obtain a permit for the transport of these snails.

SNAILS INVADE THE CLASSROOM

SNAILOPOLIS

Dear Parent,

Your child is participating in a science unit called *Snailopolis* with garden snails as the main character.

Students will have their own snail to help with the experiments, investigations, observations, and data collection. Some students become very attached to their snail during this project. Snails will be available for kids to adopt as pets. They make great pets, and they are easy to care for.

Before considering snail adoption, please read the attached Care & Requirements form.

If you decide to adopt, please fill in the form and send it back with your signature and your child's signature.

Please let me know if you have any questions.

Sincerely,

Your Child's Teacher

SNAIL CARE & REQUIREMENTS

Snails make great pets. They can live just as long as a dog, and they do not bark, meow, or oink. Snails are lots of fun to watch and they do not take a lot of work. To live comfortably in captivity, snails require the following:

- Container such as a plastic critter carrier or any container with a cover and air holes
  (Two or more snails are fine in one small container.)
- Soil, dead leaves, and/or pieces of bark
- Food dish
  (carrots, lettuce, cucumbers; most fruits and vegetables. Avoid citrus as it spoils quickly.)
- Water dish
  (wet paper towels on a plate or lid)
- A place to hide and climb. They love damp, dark places.
  (coconut shells, small branches and twigs, empty unpainted clay pots)
- Calcium for strong shells
  (cuttlebone, crushed oyster shell or boiled, crushed egg shell)

Snail Characteristics and Behaviors
- Dry air and cold weather will cause snails to become less active and perhaps hibernate.
- They have eyes but their eyesight is poor. They can smell. They cannot hear you!
- Snails lay eggs by digging a hole 2.5-4 cm deep.

Snail Care
- Wipe down the snail enclosure once a week.
- Change the substrate/soil once a month.
- Take out any rotten food and replace with fresh food every few days.

The Internet is a great source of information on snails and their care.

- -

PERMISSION FOR SNAIL ADOPTION

My child, _____, has my permission to bring home one snail to keep as a pet.

He/she will provide food, shelter, and care for the snail.

_____
Parent signature

_____
Child signature

PREPARATION FOR SNAILOPOLIS

Collect the Materials

Collect the materials listed in the MATERIALS LIST on page ix.

Store your materials in a container. A cardboard box with a cover will keep the project a mystery until the day you introduce the unit. Write "Coming Soon" or "Mystery Science" or "Can You Guess The Animal?" to build excitement and conversation.

Prepare a Habitat for Snails to Live

A large plastic container or small aquarium works well. Make sure there is a lid with holes. Place a small amount of damp garden soil, dead leaves, and/or pieces of bark at the bottom. Add a few lettuce leaves or celery, and a small jar lid with water.

Send parent notice and permission form home to parents (pages x-xi).

Hide the snail community, SNAILOPOLIS, in a secret place until it is time for the first hands-on lesson.

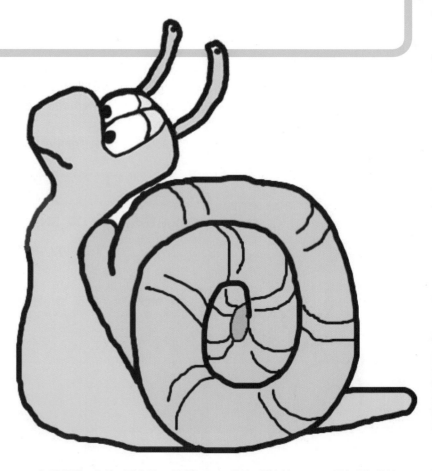

First Look: INTRODUCING SNAILS TO STUDENTS

Set Up Desks

If possible, set up desks when students are out of the room. It is so exciting to see their expressions when they walk into the room with all the "mysterious stuff" on their desks! Before students sit at their desks, ask them not to touch items on their desks until they are directed to do so.

- Put snails in individual clear plastic containers with lids. Keep them hidden until the first hands-on lesson.
- If the lesson is a secret, cover the snail containers until you are ready for students to do their research.
- Lay out newspaper on each desk. Students can work in teams of two. There are some students who may be timid about touching animals. By the end of the unit you will have some students who are quite attached to their snails.
- Lay out the items listed on page ix for each student or team of two students on the newspaper (include items in materials list with the √).

Introduction

 SAY: Today you are going to be learning about an animal that can lift ten times its own weight walking up a wall. That means that if you were as strong as this animal you would be able to carry one grizzly bear on your back, or 191 laptops, or a motorcycle, or 700 books, AND you would be able to walk straight up a wall with this 700 pound load on your back. Any guesses about which animal you will be learning about?

This animal is in most gardens. It is destructive to plants but people can eat it. Any guesses about what this animal might be?

DO: Give clues from Snail Facts (page viii) until someone guesses SNAIL.

 SAY: Today you will be learning incredible, unbelievable facts about snails. What are some things you already know about snails?

Note: Lessons 1 and 2 can be done the first day if time permits.

Lesson 1: PREDICTIONS AND FACTS

TIME: 10 minutes for introduction
10 minutes for forms

Materials
- My Snail Predictions form (page 3) ■ for Grades K-2
- Predictions and Facts form (page 4) ■ for Grades 2-4
- Pencils

Introduction

 SAY: *Raise your hand if you have seen a snail. What did it look like to you? Raise your hand if you have touched a snail. What did it feel like to you?*

 SAY: *You are going to make some predictions or guesses about snails before you actually get your own snail. Guesses are not right or wrong, they are statements that we can test. What is another word for guesses?* (Predictions.) *We can study and find out information about our predictions.*

Note: If no one comes up with the answer shown in blue, the teacher should supply it.

DO: Take out (or pass out) the grade-appropriate form, either My Snail Predictions or Predictions and Facts.

DO: Read it over together. For non-readers, the My Snail Predictions form can be done orally. Read the questions on this form and make predictions together. Non-readers can also *draw* some of their answers.

DO: Collect the forms after 10 minutes and save them until the end of Snailopolis. These forms will be used during the summary and evaluation.

My Snail Predictions

Name _____

Draw a line to show how you think a snail moves.

You breathe through your nose and mouth. Does a snail breathe through a nose or a mouth? Put an X on the place(s) you guess.

What is inside of a snail shell? Draw your guess. Put circles where you think the eyes are located.

Do you think a snail likes hot and dry weather or cold and wet weather? Draw a snail and the type of weather you guess.

Draw some things you think a snail might eat.

Does a snail have enemies? Draw your guess.

Does a snail have teeth? Make a guess/prediction.

Check one: Yes _____ No _____ If Yes, how many do you guess? _____

Predictions & Facts

Name _____

Before looking at your snail, make some guesses/predictions about snails. Write your answers in the Guesses/Predictions column. After completing all the lessons on snails, write down the facts in the Facts column. Remember that guesses are not right or wrong, they are guesses! After filling in the Guesses/Predictions turn this form in to your teacher.

	Guesses/Predictions	Facts (fill in at the end of the unit)
Do snails move in a straight line or a circle?		
Do snails have a skeleton?		
Are snails nocturnal or diurnal?		
What do snails do in hot, dry weather?		
Do snails sleep?		
How do snails breathe (lungs, through their skin, gills, other)?		
Do snails have teeth?		
What is the approximate life span?		
Are snails carnivores or herbivores?		
Do snails have eyes? How many?		
Can snails hear?		
What/who are their natural enemies?		

Box 1	Box 2
What does the bottom of a snail's "foot" look like? In Box 1 draw your guess. At the end of the unit look at the bottom of the foot. Draw what you see in Box 2.	

Lesson 2: FACT OR FICTION CARDS

TIME: 5-8 minutes

Materials
• Fact or Fiction Cards (copy pages 6-9 and cut cards)

SAY: *I am going to pass out Fact or Fiction Cards. Each card has a statement about the animal we are going to be researching. The statement on the card is either a fact or fiction. When a statement is read, point your thumb to the ceiling if you think it is a fact. Point your thumb to the floor if you think it is fiction.*

Note: All the statements are true.

Note: For students who cannot read, you can read the cards or have an older student read. Older students also love assisting with the lesson.

DO: Pass out the Fact or Fiction Cards to 12 students.

SAY: *If you have Fact or Fiction Card #1, read the statement to the class. Is this statement a fact?*

Note: After a "thumbs up/thumbs down" vote on whether the statement is a fact, the student reads the answer explanation to the class. Student with card #2 reads the statement and so on. Collect the cards when done.

Note: At the end of the lesson students can make up their own Fact or Fiction Cards using the blanks on page 9. They can see if they can come up with some fact or fiction trivia that will stump the other students.

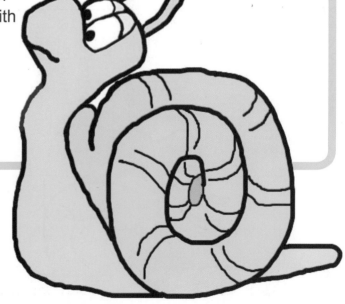

FACT or FICTION CARD #1

Snails hibernate during the winter.

Fact

Most snails hibernate during cold weather. They enclose themselves inside of their shell and seal themselves in by covering the opening with thick mucus that hardens.

FACT or FICTION CARD #2

A land snail can grow up to 12 inches.

Fact

The Ghana Tiger Snail is the largest land snail and it can grow up to 12 inches. Look at your 12 inch ruler! That's a BIG snail!

FACT or FICTION CARD #3

The largest water snail weighs more than a 3-year-old child.

Fact

The Syrinx Aruanus from Australia can grow up to 30 inches and weigh up to 40 pounds. Lay 3 rulers end to end and take away 6 inches. That is how long he would be! YIKES!!!

FACT or FICTION CARD #4

Snails have teeth.

Fact

Snails have teeth, but they are not like our teeth. Nearly all snails have radulas (RAJ u luhz). Radulas are hard, ribbonlike organs that look like tongues. Radulas contain rows of tiny teeth. Some snails have just a few teeth while others have thousands.

FACT or FICTION CARD #6

Snails can live up to 15 years in captivity.

Fact

Snails in captivity are not in danger of being eaten by birds, snakes and other predators, so they can live much longer in captivity.

FACT or FICTION CARD #8

Snails are important to our ecosystem.

Fact

Slugs and snails eat decaying plant material and fungi.

(They are also considered to be pests in gardens.)

FACT or FICTION CARD #5

Snail slime is used in medicine.

Fact

Snail slime WAS used in Ancient Greece to heal ulcers and soothe a cough. It is rich in proteins.

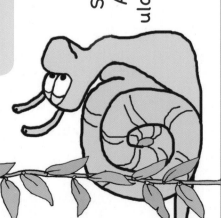

FACT or FICTION CARD #7

Snails have very poor eyesight.

Fact

Snails rely mainly on their sense of touch and smell when finding food because they have poor eyesight.

FACT or FICTION CARD #10

A snail is full grown when a small "lip" appears on the part of the shell that opens to the rest of the body.

Fact

If this lip does not appear the snail will continue to get bigger.

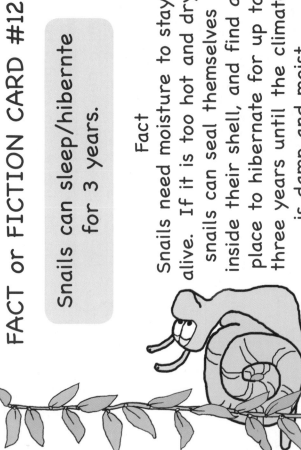

FACT or FICTION CARD #12

Snails can sleep/hibernte for 3 years.

Fact

Snails need moisture to stay alive. If it is too hot and dry, snails can seal themselves inside their shell, and find a place to hibernate for up to three years until the climate is damp and moist.

FACT or FICTION CARD #9

You can get an idea of a snail's age by counting the rings inside the shell.

Fact

Some scientists say that a snail grows one ring per year.

FACT or FICTION CARD #11

Snails cannot hear.

Fact

Snails cannot hear and they have very poor eyesight.

They rely on their sense of touch and smell to find food.

FACT or FICTION CARD
Write a statement below.

True or False?
Is your statement a fact? Write an explanation about your statement.

FACT or FICTION CARD
Write a statement below.

True or False?
Is your statement a fact? Write an explanation about your statement.

FACT or FICTION CARD
Write a statement below.

True or False?
Is your statement a fact? Write an explanation about your statement.

Lesson 3: SNAIL LABELING

TIME: 10-15 minutes

Materials
- Snail Anatomy diagram – labeled (page 11)
- Snail Anatomy diagram – not labeled student copy (page 12)
- Snails in containers
- Lay out materials for Lesson 4 also if time permits.

Note: This lesson is an introduction to Lesson 4: TOUCH-OBSERVE-RECORD.

 SAY: I am going to pass out two diagrams of a snail. The diagrams are the same except that one has labeled parts and the other does not. You will also receive your snail in a plastic container. Do Not Open The Container until you have a direction to do so. Do not shake the container or tap on it.

DO: Pass out the two Snail Anatomy diagrams. Read over and discuss.

Note: This is a short lesson. Studying the snail with the container closed will help timid students familiarize themselves with the snail without touching it.

 SAY: Using the labeled diagram, we are going to locate as many of the snail's body parts as we can. As you locate the parts on your own snail, fill in your Snail Anatomy diagram.

DO: Pass out snail containers

Note: For non-readers, today's lesson can be done orally together. The student can point to the body part on the diagram. This is also a great activity to do with an older buddy.

DO: Collect and/or put papers and snails away at the end of this lesson, or go on to Lesson 4.

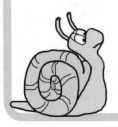

Snail Anatomy

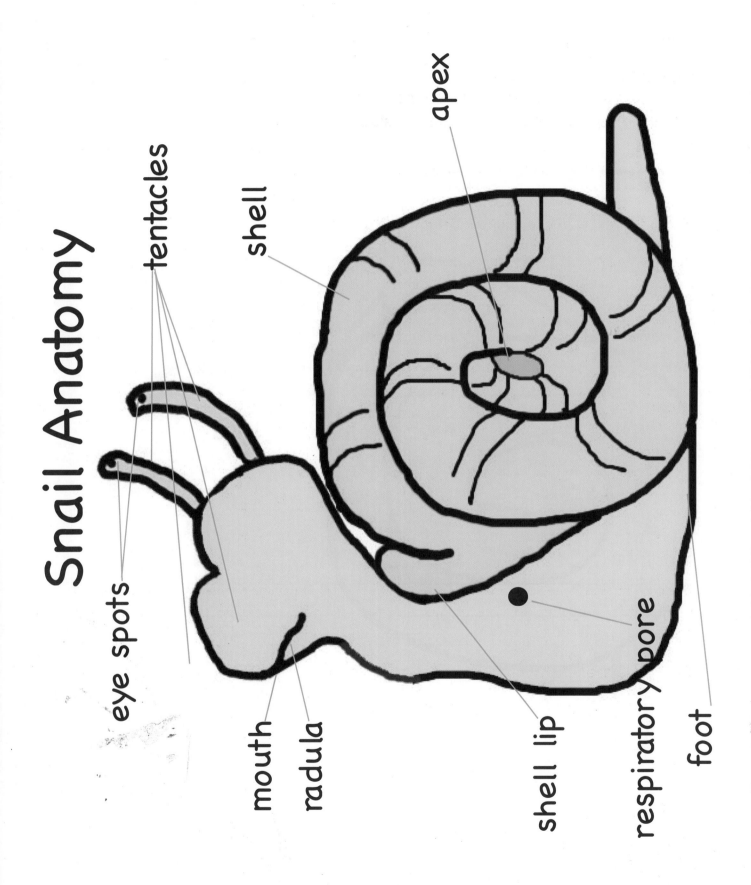

apex

tentacles

shell

eye spots

mouth

radula

shell lip

respiratory pore

foot

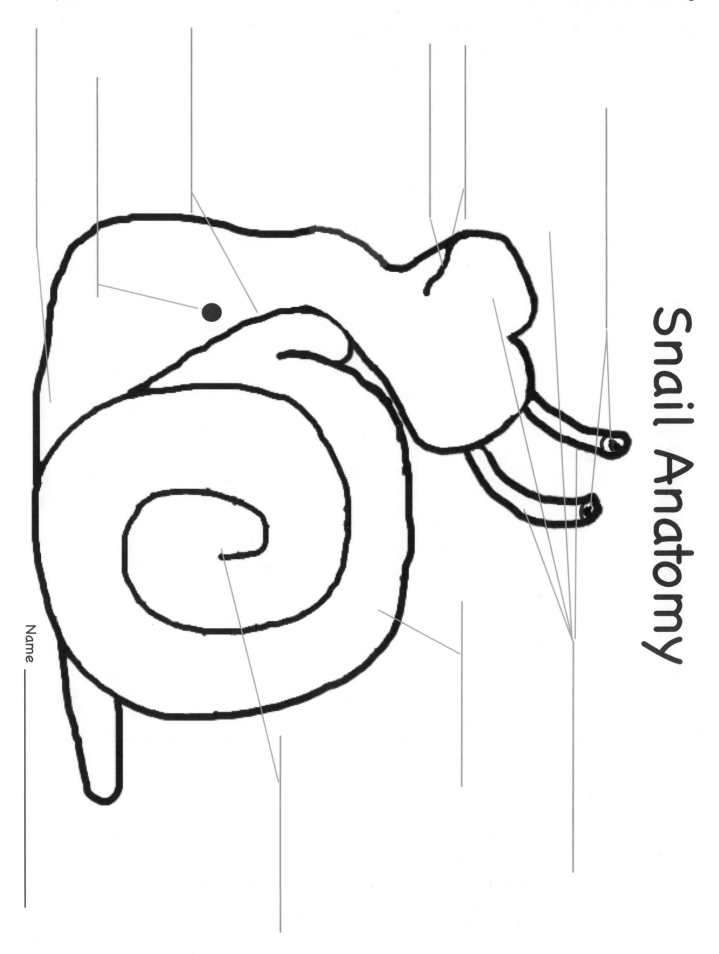

Snail Anatomy

Name

Lesson 4: **TOUCH–OBSERVE–RECORD**

TIME: 20-40 minutes

Materials
- My Snail Chart form (page 14) ■ for Grades K-2
- Touch-Observe-Record form (page 15) ■ for Grades 2-4
- Snail Anatomy – labeled diagram (page 11)
- Snails in containers
- Celery
- Items with √ from Materials List (page ix)

 SAY: What items are on your desk? (Go over the items together.) *You will use the hand lens to look at the foot, shell texture, tentacles, and patterns on the snail. I am going to give you your snail and a Touch-Observe-Record form. Your snail is in a plastic container. Can you think of some rules we need to follow to keep the snail safe? Do not shake the container or tap on it.* (Optional: *Sounds not allowed during this unit: yuck, ick, ugh, gross.*)

SAY and DEMONSTRATE:

- *When you look at the bottom of the clear container you can see the snail's foot muscle.*
- *The snail's shell is very soft. When you pick it up, its foot may cling to the container. Slide him gently, and then lift him by the shell. You can set him on your finger or hand to feel his foot muscle as he moves. Set the snail on a piece of celery to see it eat and move.*

DO: Pass out Touch-Observe-Record forms and read together.

DO: Pass out the Snail Anatomy labeled diagram and go over together.

DO: Pass out snails and have students touch, observe, and record on the forms.

Note: For non-readers, this form can be done orally together. You can use a projector so students can see you fill in the graph. If available, have older students assist younger students. They will be learning too.

DO: At the end of this lesson have students put their snails in the plastic container with a fresh piece of lettuce and collect until the next lesson. If the next lesson is more than a day away put snails in the habitat you created (Snailopolis).

DO: If students get attached to their snails (and they do) you can put a dot of ink on their shells or write names on containers with permanent markers.

 SAY: What are some things you observed?

TOUCH-OBSERVE-RECORD: MY SNAIL CHART

Name _____

Use a hand lens to study your snail. Read each question.
Mark one box for each of the things you see or inches you measure.
Be sure to look at your snail to answer the questions.

Snail	1	2	3	4	5	6	7	8	More than 8
How many creases on the shell?									
How many tentacles?									
How many eyes?									
How many inches tall is the shell?									
How many inches wide is the shell?									
How many inches did the snail move in 30 seconds?									
How long is the snail's foot?									
How many colors can you count on the snail's shell and body?									

TOUCH-OBSERVE-RECORD

Name _____

Use a hand lens to observe your snail.

SHELL

Examine the shape of the shell. What geometric shape is it similar to? _____ Touch the shell. What does it feel like? _____

Is the shell hard or soft? _____ Is the shell smooth or rough? _____ Look at the color and patterns in the shell.

Draw what you see.

TENTACLES

How many tentacles does your snail have? _____
Use a hand lens to examine the ends of the longest tentacles. The eyes are at the end of the longest tentacles. Gently touch the end of one long tentacle. What did you notice? Can it move one tentacle at a time or do both move at the same time? _____ Examine the shortest tentacles. The snail uses these tentacles to smell and feel. Why do you think the "smell-feel" tentacles are shorter than the eye tentacles? _____

Draw one of the eye tentacles.

STOMACH-FOOT

Use the hand lens to examine the bottom of the foot. Draw what you see. Look for the ripples. How does the foot feel? _____ Lift the container and look at the snail from underneath. Draw what you see in the box. Can you find the breathing hole (pneumostome)? Look near the opening of the shell.

Draw what you see.

What is the height of the shell? _____ How long are the eye tentacles? _____ How wide is the shell? _____ How long are the smell-touch tentacles? _____ How long is the snail's foot? _____

How many colors can you count on the snail's body and shell? _____

Draw your own snail on a separate sheet of paper and label its parts.

Lesson 5: SNAILOPOLIS SPEEDWAY

TIME: 20-40 minutes

Materials
- Snails in containers
- Snail name tags (page 17)
- Snail Power Experiment form (page 18)
- Small nut cups
- Scotch tape
- Lettuce
- Scale if available (to weigh snails)
- Pennies or washers (pennies weigh approximately 2.5 grams.

 SAY: *Can a snail really haul up to 10 times their own weight? You are about to find out for yourself. You have a blank snail name tag on your desk. Think of a name for your snail and write the name on the card. Be creative.*

 SAY: *You are going to investigate to see how much weight your snail can pull. Let's read through the investigation together.*

DO: Read Snail Power (page 18) and do the steps together until the students understand the activity.

DO: Older students can do the math problem to find out how much weight they could pull if they were as strong as a snail.

Note: Have older children or a volunteer do the math problem for younger children. Also, it might be easier to choose an average weight for your grade level instead of using the actual weight of each student.

DO: At the end of the session, share observations.

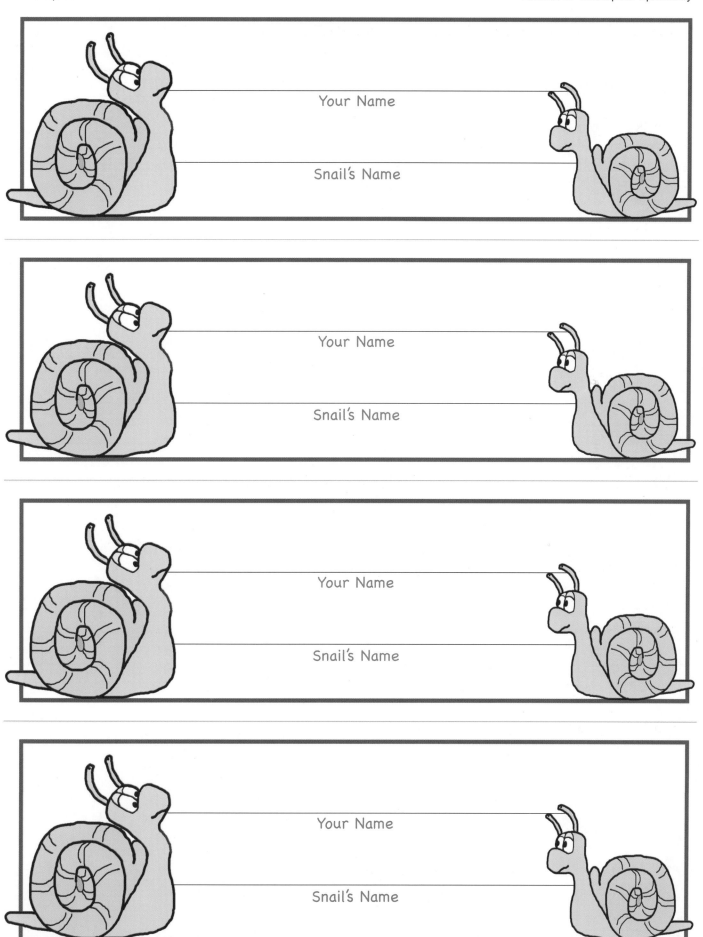

Your Name

Snail's Name

Your Name

Snail's Name

Your Name

Snail's Name

Your Name

Snail's Name

SNAIL POWER EXPERIMENT

Name _____

How Much Weight Can Your Snail Pull?

Let's find out.

Materials
• Small paper cup
• Scotch tape – about 2–3 inches
• Small washers, pennies, or buttons

Steps
1. Put a piece of lettuce at one end of the speedway.
2. Put the snail at the other end.
3. Put a piece of tape on the edge of a paper cup.
4. Tape the other edge to the back of your snail shell.
5. Drop in pennies/washers one at a time.
6. Wait and watch for your snail to slide.

Math Problem

How much do you weigh?

Write that number below.

Multiply your weight by 50.

Write your weight here →

$$\begin{array}{r} \square \\ \times 50 \\ \hline \square\square\square \\ 000 \\ + \square\square\square \leftarrow \\ \hline \square\square\square\square \end{array}$$

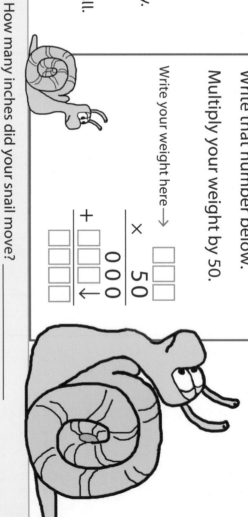

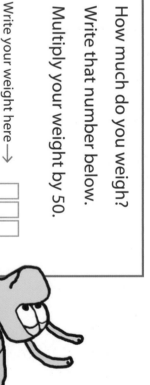

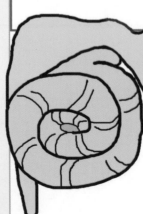

Start time _____

End time _____

How many inches did your snail move? _____

Snailopolis 500 Speedway

Lettuce

Start

Snails can haul up to 10 times their own weight when crawling up a vertical surface. When gliding along horizontally, they can carry up to 50 times their weight.

If you were as strong as a snail, you would be able to pull _____ pounds.

Write the answer to your math problem on the line above.

An elephant weighs 3,000 pounds. So does a car.

Lesson 6: SNAILOPOLITAN MUSEUM OF ART

TIME: 20-40 minutes

Materials
- Snailopolitan Art form (page 20)
- Artist's Biography form (page 21) and sample (page 22)
- Snails
- Paper plates
- Washable poster paint
  (One color per plate. Red looks a little like blood. You might want to stick with blue, green, orange or purple.)

SAY: *Have you ever been to a museum of art or an art show? How would you explain a museum of art to someone who had never been inside a museum? What kind of art would go in a museum of art?*

Note: A masterpiece refers to a creation that has been given critical praise. It might be an artist's greatest work, or it might be recognized as having outstanding creativity, skill, or workmanship.

SAY: *Your snail has been invited to display an original painting in the Snailopolitan Museum of Art. I am going to pass out the form it will use to create its masterpiece.*

DO: Pass out the Snailopolitan Art form and read together.

DO: Pass out paper plates with small amounts of colored, washable poster paint.

SAY: *Your snail is going to paint a masterpiece with its foot. Pick up your snail* <u>*gently*</u> *and set its foot in the paint. Next set the snail on the art paper.*

DO: Demonstrate.

DO: After the paintings are done, pass out the Artist's Biography and sample forms.

SAY: *Now fill out the Artist's Biography. Look at the example form to get the idea.*

Note: When the paintings are dry students can write the name of the painting and the artist's name. These works of art look great when backed with black construction paper.

Note: A Snailopolitan Art Show bulletin board is almost a must. Beneath each work of art you can display the artist's biography.

Name _____

SNAILOPOLITAN ART

Your snail has been invited to display an original painting in the Snailopolitan Museum of Art. Gently dip Snail's foot in washable paint. Set the snail in the center of the frame. You might encourage the snail's creativity with a piece of lettuce. Allow 20 or 30 minutes. When the painting is complete, rinse paint off the snail's foot. Title the painting and write the snail's name. Color or decorate the frame.

Painting Name _____

Artist's Name _____

Name _____

ARTIST'S BIOGRAPHY

Illustration of the Artist

_____
Artist's Name

_____
Age

Names of Best Known Paintings

_____

_____

Things That Influence This Painter to Paint

_____

_____

Awards Received

_____

ARTIST'S BIOGRAPHY

Illustration of the Artist

Leonardo da Snail
Artist's Name

365 days
Age

Names of Best Known Paintings

Snail on a Plate

Snail Without a Shell

Walking in Circles

Things That Influence This Painter to Paint

lettuce

cold, rainy days

Awards Received

New Artist of the Year and **Best in Mollusk Category**

Lesson 7: VENN DIAGRAM: Snails and Me

TIME: 20-40 minutes

Materials
  • Venn diagram (page 24)
  • Pencils

 SAY: *How are you and a snail the same? Different? Consider eyes, nose,*
mouth, feet, communication, coloring, heart, organs, artistic ability. Be creative.

DO: Pass out the Venn diagram. Read together. Younger students can draw pictures.

Note: Working in teams of two is fun. Students brainstorm together, and then fill in
their own form. Encourage listing as many traits as possible in each space.

DO: Share.

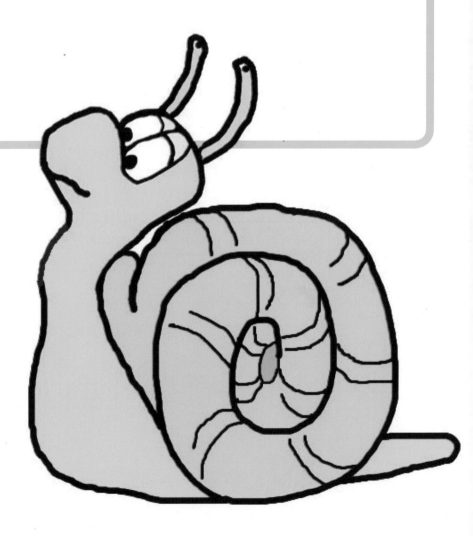

23

Name _____

Same or Different
Snails & Me

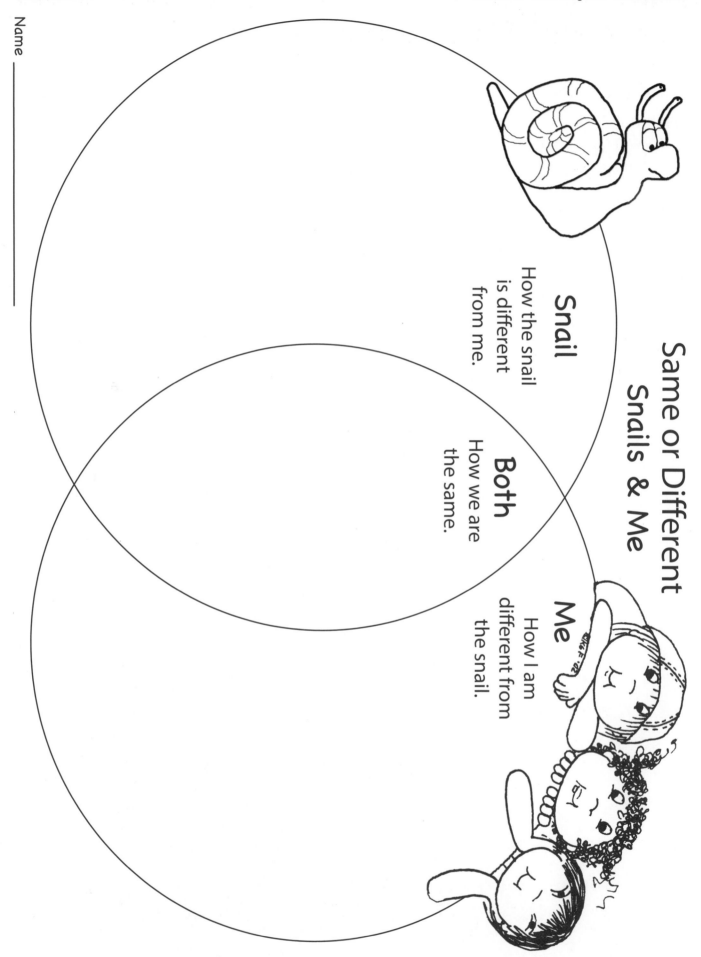

Snail
How the snail
is different
from me.

Both
How we are
the same.

Me
How I am
different from
the snail.

Lesson 8: SNAILBOT INVENTIONS

TIME: 20-40 minutes

Materials
- Snails (optional)
- Snailbot Invention form (page 26)
- Snailbot Description form (page 27)
- Pencils
- Crayons

 SAY: *You will be asked to invent a snail robot using geometric shapes. Raise your hand to share what you know about robots.*

 SAY: *The word robot comes from a Czech word that means "forced work or labor." A robot is a man-made machine that can perform work or actions that people normally do. Robots can make candy, build cars, explore the ocean floor, land on the moon, or perform surgeries. A robot can be a toy and just provide entertainment.*

Sometimes using a robot is cheaper and easier than using humans to do work.

Most robots have a "brain" or control center like a computer. They might have wheels, gears, motors, pulleys; all kinds of mechanical parts. They may even have a sensor, like robotic vacuum cleaners, that lets it "sense" if there is a wall nearby. It might even be controlled by voice commands. Let's list some geometric shapes.

Can you see any shapes on your snail that look a bit like a geometric shape?
(oval shell, rectangular eye stalks, oval foot, circular eyes)

DO: List names and show samples of geometric shapes.

 SAY: *What could a snail robot do? Could the snailbot's shell be empty? Could it chew up crumbs on the floor with its thousands of teeth better than a vacuum cleaner? Could it clean your room? What about a snailbot that was as big as a house? Could a snailbot have a door in the shell that people could enter? What would be inside? How about a snailbot that was a form of transportation.*

DO: Pass out the Snailbot Invention and Snailbot Description forms.

 SAY: *Design a snailbot. Use five or more geometric shapes to create your Snailbot. Then use the Snailbot Description form to describe your invention.*

SNAILBOT INVENTION

SNAILBOT: Geometic Shapes
Invent a snail robot using geometric shapes. Use 5 or more shapes to invent your snailbot? Here are just a few shapes you might use.

Name _____ Your snailbot's name _____

SNAILBOT DESCRIPTION

An invention is something that solves a problem, makes things safer, or provides entertainment. It might be as big as a house or as small as a dot on a piece of paper. It might be a form of transportation, a dwelling, a game, something to wear, a food, playground equipment, etc.—anything that has never been created before. Kids invented ear muffs, the trampoline, and the popsicle. You created a Snailbot. Tell a little about your new invention.

Inventor's Name _____

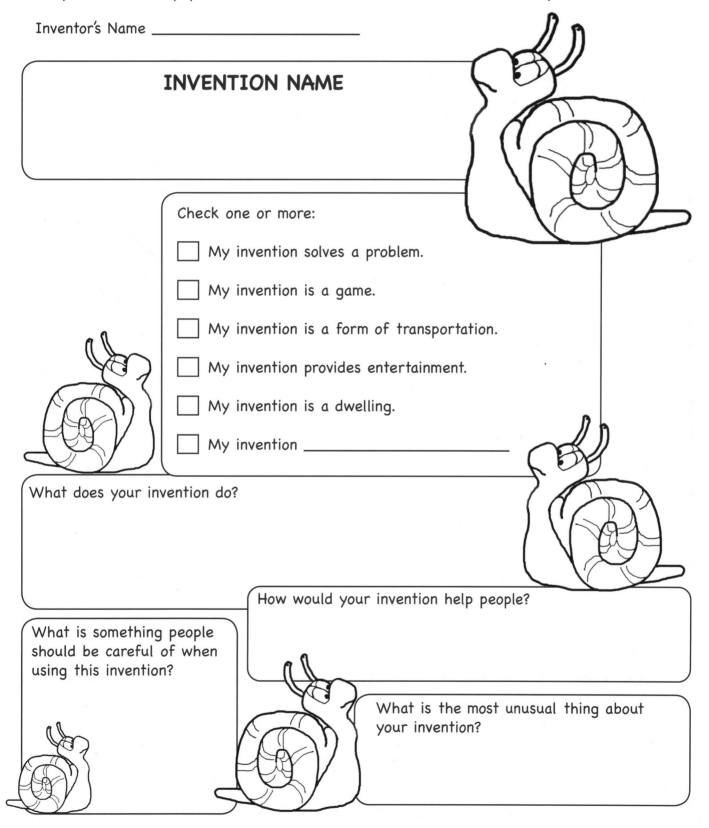

INVENTION NAME

Check one or more:

☐ My invention solves a problem.

☐ My invention is a game.

☐ My invention is a form of transportation.

☐ My invention provides entertainment.

☐ My invention is a dwelling.

☐ My invention _____

What does your invention do?

How would your invention help people?

What is something people should be careful of when using this invention?

What is the most unusual thing about your invention?

Lesson 9: SNAILOPOLIS NEWS Projects

TIME: Varies

Materials
- Newpaper samples
- Snailopolis News Topics form (page 29)

Note: This lesson includes several activities. The materials for each activity are listed on a separate Teacher Page.

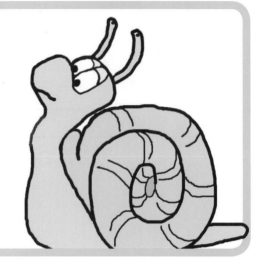

Newspapers and News Articles

DO: Pass out one page of a newspaper to every two students.

 SAY: *Look over the page for 60 seconds and be ready to share three things you noticed about lettering, layout, pictures, article author, headings, etc.*

DO: Explain the elements of a news page.

DO: Share observations and pass out the News Topics form. Read over and discuss together.

Note: You can decide to have students choose one of the projects from the News Topics form, or you may choose to have all students participate in the same project.

Discussion

Preface each activity with discussion on news articles.

 SAY: *There are certain elements common to most news articles.*

- a **Headline** or title
- a **Byline** which tells who wrote the article
- the **Location** where the article is written
- a **Lead Paragraph** which is found at the beginning of the article and briefly answers the questions "who," "what," "when," "why," "where," "how"
- **Supporting Paragraphs** that follow the lead paragraph and give more information, details, or quotes

Snailopolis News Topics

Below are some newspaper topics you might find in a Snailopolis newspaper.

SENSATIONAL SNAILS

Did you know there are over 200,000 species of mollusks, including snails? Some can grow up to 30 inches long!

• Do some research and find out more about snails.

• Write an informational article or a fictional article about this amazing animal.

• Illustrate it.

SNAIL CONTEST WINNER

Congratulations!

Your snail shell design won a blue ribbon in this year's contest.

• Draw a picture of your prize-winning design.

THE FABLE OF THE SNAIL

The Snailberry Medal Award goes to the author of the most distinguished snail novel for children.

You are the winner for your story, *The Fable of the Snail*.

• Write the first paragraph from your story.

HELP WANTED!

There is a new job opening for a Snailologist on Snail Island.

• Write a short newspaper advertisement for the job.

  Include the qualifications needed for this job.

IN MY OPINION

If you were a snail, would you rather live in the ocean or an aquarium?

Explain your answer.

SNAILOPOLIS NEWS Projects: News Flash

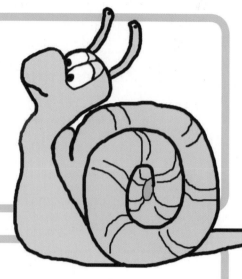

TIME: Varies

Materials
- Snailopolis News Topics form (page 29)
- Snailopolis News Flash student form (page 31)
- Pencils
- Crayons

REVIEW

  SAY: *There are certain elements common to most news articles.*

- *a **Headline** or title*
- *a **Byline** which tells who wrote the article*
- *the **Location** where the article is written*
- *a **Lead Paragraph** which is found at the beginning of the article and briefly answers the questions "who," "what," "when," "why," "where," "how"*
- ***Supporting Paragraphs** that follow the lead paragraph and give more information, details, or quotes.*

NEWS FLASH Introduction

  SAY: *You work for the local newspaper in Snailopolis. You have been asked to write an article on a breaking story in the city of Snailopolis.*

DO: Pass out and discuss the SNAILOPOLIS NEWS FLASH Student Form.

SNAILOPOLIS NEWS FLASH

Write an article on one of the following topics:

- Snails in Space
- Snailopolis Students Ask, "Do We Really Need Homework?"
- Snailopolis Candidates Running for President

Most newspaper articles include the answers to the questions below. Answer the questions to help you write your article.

Who: _____

What: _____

When: _____

Where: _____

Why: _____

How: _____

News Flash

by _____

_____

_____

_____

_____

_____

_____

_____

_____

_____

SNAILOPOLIS NEWS Projects: News Article

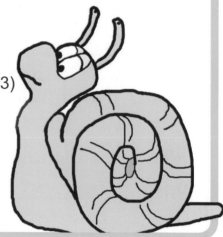

TIME: Varies

Materials
- Snailopolis News Topics form (page 29)
- Snailopolis News Article: Sensational Snails form (page 33)
- Pencils
- Crayons

REVIEW

 SAY: There are certain elements common to most news articles.

- a **Headline** or title
- a **Byline** which tells who wrote the article
- the **Location** where the article is written
- a **Lead Paragraph** which is found at the beginning of the article and briefly answers the questions "who," "what," "when," "why," "where," "how"
- **Supporting Paragraphs** that follow the lead paragraph and give more information, details or quotes

NEWS ARTICLE Introduction

 SAY: You work for the local newspaper in Snailopolis and you have been asked to write an article on Sensational Snails. You can illustrate your article or take a photo of a real snail and attach it to your article.

DO: Pass out and discuss the Snailopolis News Topics form and the News Article form.

SNAILOPOLIS NEWS: News Article

Did you know there are over 200,000 species of mollusks, including snails? Some can grow up to 30 inches long! Do some research and find out more about snails. Write an informational article about this amazing animal and illustrate it, or take a photo of a real snail and glue it below.

Sensational Snails
by

_____

_____

_____

_____

_____

_____

_____

_____

_____

_____

SNAILOPOLIS NEWS Projects: City Newspaper

TIME: Varies

Materials
- News Topics (page 29)
- Newspaper Sample (page 35)
- Newspaper Template (page 36)
- Pencils
- Crayons

CITY NEWSPAPER

SAY: You are the editor of the Snailopolis News. The citizens of Snailopolis read your paper to find out about what is happening in the city of Snailopolis. Your newspaper is due to go out on _____. You can include:

- *Advertisements to sell products that citizens of Snailopolis would buy*
- *Dates for upcoming Snailopolis events, swap meets, farmer's markets*
- *Work ads*
- *School events, sports, government news, marches, parades, etc.*
- *Cartoon strips*
- *Photos*
- *Drawings*

DO: Pass out and discuss the Snailopolis News Topics form, the Newspaper Sample form, and the Newspaper Template form.

Note: This project works well in teams of 2-4 students.

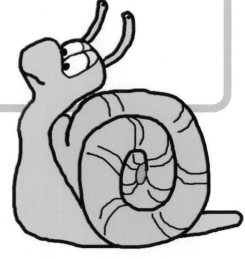

SNAILOPOLIS NEWS

www.snailopolisdaily.com   WORLD'S FAVORITE SNAIL NEWSPAPER   Since 1515

Local Snails Win Science Award

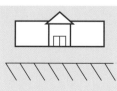

Special Project Brings Honor to Snailopolis Elementary School

Use one of the articles from your Snailopolis News projects here. Write your own headline for it and include a picture or drawing.

_____ _____

_____ _____

_____ _____

_____

_____ _____ _____

_____ _____ _____

_____ _____ _____

Are You Drinking Enough Snail Slime?

Use one of the articles from your Snailopolis News projects here. Write your own headline for it and include a picture or drawing.

Doctors, ancient philosophers, nutrition experts extol health benefits.

Find out where to get it for less.
Page C2

Snail Suspect Leads Cops on Very Low-Speed Chase

Use one of the articles from your Snailopolis News projects here. Write your own headline for it and include a picture or drawing.

Suspect

City Council Explores Expanding Parking at Snailopolis Art Museum

Use one of the articles from your Snailopolis News projects here. Write your own headline for it and include a picture or drawing.

Lesson 10: The TORTOISE, the HARE, and the SNAIL

TIME: 10-15 minutes for introduction
Writing time varies

Materials
- Story: *The Tortoise and the Hare* (check your library)
- Story Map (page 38) ■ for Grades K-2
- Story Map (page 39) ■ for Grades 2-4
- *The Tortoise, the Hare, and the Snail* story writing paper (page 40)

Background
The Tortoise and the Hare is one of Aesop's Fables about a race between a slow-moving tortoise and a very proud hare. When a tortoise challenges a rabbit to a race, the rabbit accepts, convinced he cannot lose. Even the slowest tortoise can defeat a fast-moving hare. How about a slow-moving snail?

Introduction
 SAY: How many of you remember hearing the story of <u>The Tortoise and the Hare</u>? What kind of story is it? (fable) *I am going to read the story. At the end of the story I am going to ask you to share as many characteristics as you can about each character in the story. What is a characteristic?* (trait, feature, mannerism of person, place, thing)

DO: Read the story.

 SAY: What are the characteristics of the hare? (fast, nimble, impatient, proud, arrogant, boastful) *What are the characteristics of the tortoise?* (slow, determined, does not give up, patient) *Who won the race and why?*

 SAY: What facts do you remember about how a snail moves?
(glides • slow • powered by contracting muscles in its foot
- slime produced allows the snail to glide on surfaces that are sharp and pointy
- does not usually move in a straight line)

 SAY: If a snail took part in the race how might the story change? You are going to write a fable. It will be called <u>The Tortoise, the Hare, and the Snail</u>.

DO: Pass out the Story Map form and read over together. Fill in the page together or separately.

 SAY: Use the story map to write your story on the writing paper.

Name _____   **Story Map**

Main Characters	Setting	Supporting Characters

Beginning

Middle

End

Name _____ **Story Map**

Main Characters	Setting	Supporting Characters

Problem or Conflict

Resolution or Outcome

Write a brief summary of the story and/or the lesson learned.

Title

by

Lesson 11: **FIRST DAY OF SCHOOL**

TIME: 15-20 minutes for introduction
Writing time varies

Materials

- First Day of School form (page 42) ■ for Grades K-2
- First Day of School story writing paper (page 43) ■ for Grades 2-4
- Pencils
- Crayons

Introduction

SAY: *What do you remember about your first day of school? Do you remember your teacher? What was it like? Were you nervous? Did you meet new friends?*

Note:

1) Grades 2-4 students may want to write a story that can be read to Grades K-2 students.

2) Encourage more experienced writers to review and select from the following types of writing:

Fiction: a story about imaginary characters and events.
Fable: a story giving a useful truth, especially in which animals speak as humans.
Humor: a story filled with fun, excitement, meant to entertain
Poetry: verse and rhythmic writing
Tall Tale: a humorous story with exaggerations and heroes who do the impossible.

DO: Pass out the First Day Of School form ■ (K-2) and read over together.
Pass out the bordered story writing paper ■ (2-4).

DO: Share stories.

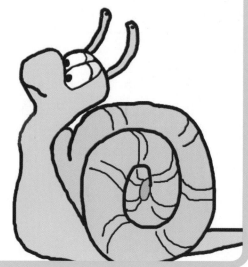

FIRST DAY OF SCHOOL

Name _____

Remember your first day of school? Nemo, the 6-year-old fish in the movie called *Finding Nemo*, was ready to go to school, meet new friends, and go on adventures. Tell about your snail's first day of school.

My snail's name is _____

My snail is _____ years old.

My snail wants to learn about _____.

My snail's favorite food is _____.

Something special about my snail is _____

My snail is really good at _____

_____

_____

This is a picture of my snail on the first day of snail school.

First Day of School

SNAILOPOLIS ELEMENTARY SCHOOL

Welcome

Kindergarten Snails

Name

Lesson 12: SNAIL LIFE CYCLE

TIME: 10-15 minutes

Materials
- Life Cycle of a Garden Snail form (page 45)
- Life Cycle of a Garden Snail answer sheet (page 46)
- Pencils
- Crayons
- Optional: Book on snails (See Snail Book Nook, page 61)

Background

A snail reaches adulthood at about two years. At three years of age a snail can lay about 85 eggs at a time up to six times per year. In warm, damp weather snails dig a hole 2.5 to 4 cm deep and lay white or yellowish, small, round eggs in the dirt. When an egg hatches, a small snail emerges with a very thin, soft, almost transparent shell. The first thing the baby snail does is eat. It eats its eggshell and possibly any eggs that have not hatched. As the snail grows, its shell grows with it.

 SAY: *Do you think a snail hatches from an egg, or do you think they are born alive? What do you think is the first thing a baby snail does? Let's find out.*

DO: Pass out the Life Cycle form.

 SAY: *Look at the Life Cycle of a Garden Snail. Let's read it over together.*

DO: READ and discuss.

 SAY: *As I read some facts about a snail's life cycle you can check off the correct answer or fill in a word that completes the sentence. You will have extra time to fill in the blanks, and then you can color the pictures.*

DO: Read the background info above as students fill in the blanks. Share answers and correct as needed.

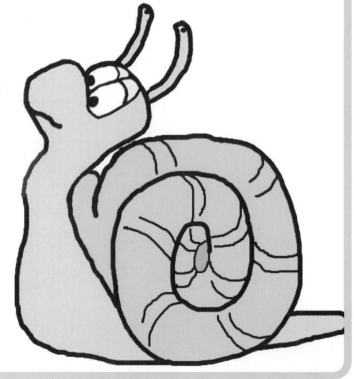

Name _____

LIFE CYCLE of a GARDEN SNAIL

(Fill in a word or put a √ next to the correct answers.)

4 ADULT

a. A snail begins to lay eggs at about ____ years of age.

b. A garden snail might lay eggs ____ in a can
____ in a hole in the ground ____ on top of the ground.

3 YOUNG ADULT

a. A snail reaches adulthood at about ____ years of age.

b. As a snail grows ...
____ its shell grows with it.
____ its shell falls off and the snail grows a new one.
____ it crawls out of the shell when it gets too small.

1 EGGS

a. Snail eggs are ____ white ____ yellowish ____ purple.

b. How many times can a snail lay eggs in one year?
____ 2 ____ 6 ____ 100

c. How many eggs does a snail usually lay at one time?
____ 1 ____ 15 ____ 85 ____ 2,000

2 BABY

a. A baby snail has a ____ hard shell ____ soft shell ____ no shell.

b. As soon as it hatches the baby snail
____ eats its eggshell ____ eats a flower ____ takes a walk.

c. A baby snail's shell is
____ as hard as a rock ____ very soft.

LIFE CYCLE of a GARDEN SNAIL
Answer Page

1 EGGS

a. Snail eggs are __√__ white __√__ yellowish ___ purple.

b. How many times can a snail lay eggs in one year?

___ 2 __√__ 6 ___ 100

c. How many eggs does a snail usually lay at one time?

___ 1 ___ 15 __√__ 85 ___ 2,000

2 BABY

a. A baby snail has a ___ hard shell __√__ soft shell ___ no shell.

b. As soon as it hatches the baby snail

__√__ eats its eggshell ___ eats a flower ___ takes a walk.

c. A baby snail's shell is

___ as hard as a rock __√__ very soft.

3 YOUNG ADULT

a. A snail reaches adulthood at about __2__ years of age.

b. As a snail grows …

__√__ its shell grows with it.

___ its shell falls off and the snail grows a new one.

___ it crawls out of the shell when it gets too small.

4 ADULT

a. A snail begins to lay eggs at about __3__ years of age.

b. A garden snail might lay eggs ___ in a can

__√__ in a hole in the ground ___ on top of the ground.

Lesson 13: SNAILOPOLIS COMMUNITY

TIME: Varies depending on the topics and activities you choose

Materials
- Snail Community Story Map (page 48)
- Story writing paper (pages 49-54)

 SAY: *If someone asked you to define the word community, what would you say?* (A community is a group of people living together in one place.)

 SAY: *What is the name of your city or community? Name some things in your community.* (Students might name houses, animals, parks, gas stations, churches, trees, stores, airports, banks, farms, roads, schools, hospitals, street lights.)

 SAY: *The story about* <u>Curious George</u> *takes place in a city. Nemo lives in an ocean community.* <u>A Bug's Life</u>, <u>Bambi</u>, <u>Madagascar</u>, *and* <u>The Lion King</u> *are stories that take place in a community of talking animals.*

 SAY: *When the authors created the story about Nemo they used fact **and** fiction to create their story. Nemo is a talking fish who is old enough to go to school (fiction). Fish live in the ocean (fact).*

If you were asked to create a community with talking snails and other animals what fact and fiction things could you include? Would you have a government run by Snailopolins? How would Snailopolis be ruled: king? queen? president? kids? What is the natural habitat of garden snails? What do they eat? Would you have stores? What would Snailopolins purchase: decorations for their shells? new forms of transportation? glasses? What are their natural enemies? What happens when the temperature is too hot or too cold? What kind of celebrations might a snail community have? What might the citizens of Snailopolis do if they heard that humans were hunting for snails to make escargot for a big feast?

Could you rewrite the movie called <u>Frozen</u> *so the main characters were snails? How about a story called* <u>The Snail King</u>. *Recall the amazing facts in the Fact or Fiction cards at the beginning of the unit. Might you add some of those facts in your story?*

DO: Have the students complete the story map or begin the creative writing project. Teams of two sometimes work well when brainstorming and writing the story. Some students might ask to create a play.

DO: Pass out the story writing paper and let the students pick the one they want to use.

Snail Community Story Map

A community is a group of people who share the same things, such as where they live, culture, language, beliefs, interests, and a way of life. A rural community is outside of a city. It may be a small town or farming community. An urban community is like a city or large town. Think about these things when you create your community: 1) citizen's rights 2) responsibility 3) helping to make decisions 4) cooperation 5) plants and animals 6) services 7) traditions 8) tourists 9) weather conditions and seasons 10) community location

Name of developer: _____

COMMUNITY NAME

What will your community be like?

☐ This community will be in the country.

☐ This community will be in the city.

☐ This community will have roads.

☐ This community will have parks.

☐ This community will have libraries.

☐ This community will have schools.

List some of the jobs available in your community.

How will the citizens get food? Will they use money or trade things to get what they need?

Will your community have a mayor, a sheriff, or a president?

What will citizens do to relax?

Title _____

by _____

Title

by

_____

Title

_____

by

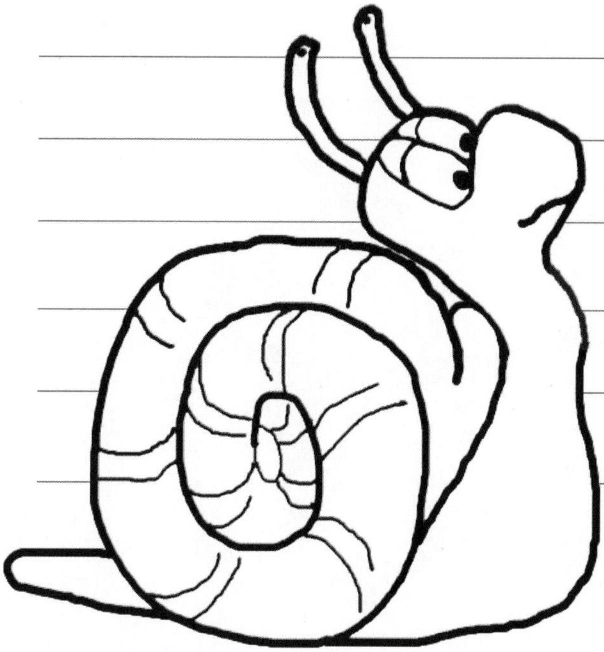

_____

_____

_____

_____

_____

_____

_____

_____

_____

_____

_____

_____

_____

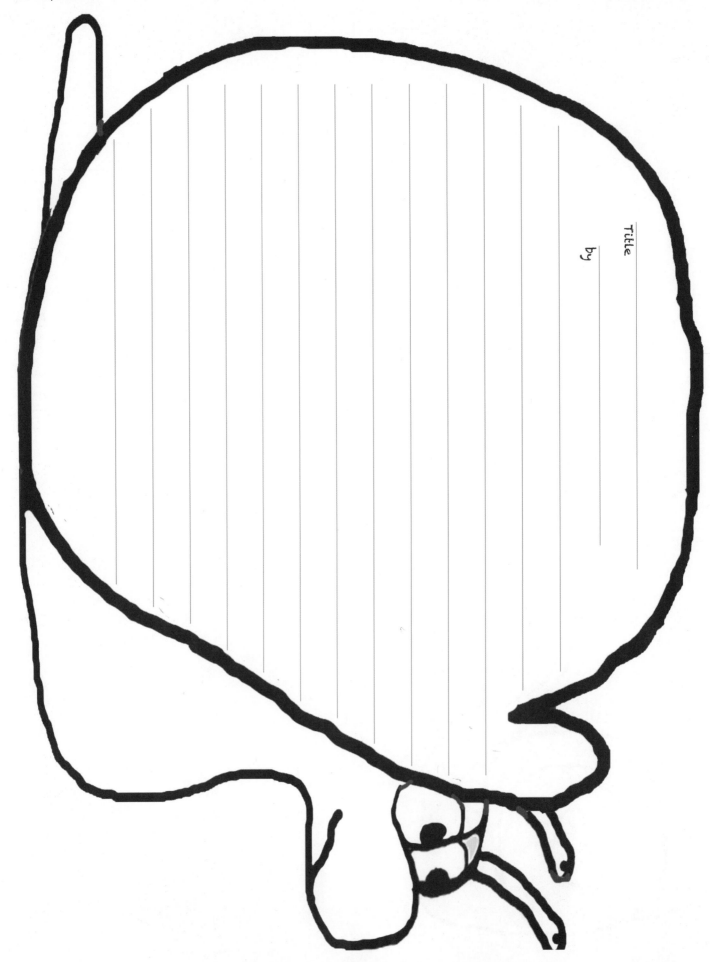

Title

by

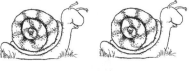

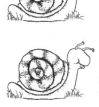

Title _____

by _____

_____

_____

_____

_____

_____

_____

_____

_____

_____

_____

_____

_____

_____

_____

_____

_____

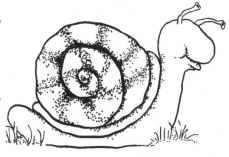

Name _____   Story Title _____

TELL A STORY
Who are the characters in this picture? Where does it take place? What might be
happening? Do the characters look scared? Surprised? Annoyed? Who is the main character?
Is there a problem to be solved? Use your imagination to write a story about the picture
below. Will your story include FACT and FICTION? Will it be a fairy tale, myth, or legend?

SUMMARY AND EVALUATION

TIME: 10 minutes for introduction
10-15 minutes for forms

Materials

- My Snail Predictions forms ■ (Grades K-2) (from beginning of unit, page 3)
- Predictions and Facts forms ■ (Grades 2-4) (from beginning of unit, page 4)
- My Snail Facts form ■ (Grades K-2) (page 56)
- Snail Anatomy diagram – not labeled (page 57)
- Fact or Fiction Cards – blank cards (page 9)
- Pencils

Introduction

SAY: *You made some predictions about snails and filled in your guesses and predictions at the beginning of this unit. You have researched, collected data, and experimented to find out about snails. I am going to pass out the papers you filled in at the beginning of the unit. Look at your predictions and then fill in the facts. You will also receive a Snail Anatomy diagram. See how many labels you can fill in.*

Note: Consider having students fill in their own papers but discuss and work together in teams of two.

DO: Pass out the forms students filled in at the beginning of the unit. Pass out new Snail Anatomy diagrams (not labeled).

Note: The students who used the page called <u>My Snail Predictions</u> will need the new page called <u>My Snail Facts</u> to fill in.

DO: Students can work in teams of two to create their own Fact or Fiction Cards using the blank Fact or Fiction Cards.

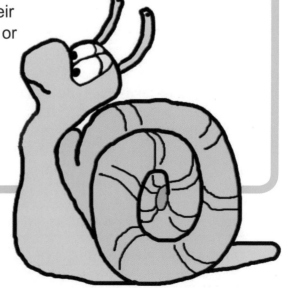

My Snail Facts

Name _____

> Draw a line to show how you think a snail moves.

You breathe through your nose and mouth.
Does a snail breathe through a nose or
mouth? Put an X on the place(s).

What is inside of a SNAIL SHELL?
Draw your guess. Put circles where
the eyes are located.

Does a snail likes hot and dry weather or cold and wet weather?
Draw a snail and the type of weather it likes.

Draw some things a snail might eat.

What are a snail's enemies?
Draw an enemy.

Does a snail have teeth?
Check one: _____ Yes _____ No If "Yes," how many? _____

Snail Anatomy

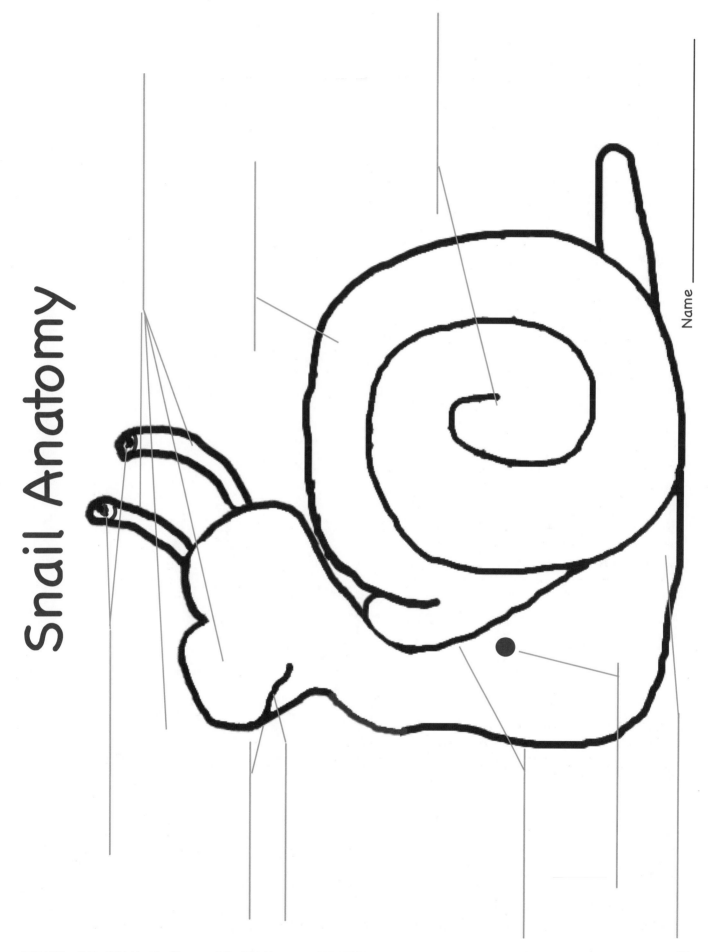

Name

SNAILOPOLIS CELEBRATION

TIME: 40-60 minutes

Materials
- Snailopolis Celebration invitations (page 59)
- Celebration suggestions (see below)

Note: Having a celebration to share the projects is a MUST! Parents will be fascinated with the activities their children participated in.

SUGGESTIONS

1) Students can color the invitations before taking them home.

2) Students brainstorm types of snacks for celebration but give them Snailopolis names. (Cookies • Granola • Pizza • Juice • Popcorn • Licorice)

3) Arrange to have parents send food with their child the morning of the celebration.

4) Prior to party, students make up Snailopolis food names to be placed by food and drinks. (Eye-spot cookies • Snailopcorn • Snizza • Shell-ola (granola) • Snailjuice)

5) The day of the celebration students set up their desks with their snail environment, snail name label, and packet with their experiments and projects.

6) Create a bulletin board (you may have already created a board) displaying some of the projects.

7) When parents arrive, have a student welcome them.

8) Have parents participate in the FACT or FICTION CARDS activity. Students read the Teacher Page "SAY" to parents.

9) Have each student select a project to share aloud.

10) Have students stand by their desks as parents rotate around the room to observe and ask questions.

11) Consider having younger grades visit Snailopolis also.

YOU ARE INVITED

Snailopolis Is Having a Celebration

Date

Time

Location

Meet Snailopolins
Visit Snailopolitan Museum of Art
View Snailbot Inventions
Meet Snail Authors
Read The Local Snailopolis News

Refreshments Served

THANK YOU FOR YOUR DONATION

Date _____

Dear _____

_____

_____

_____

_____

_____

_____

_____

_____

_____

_____

SNAIL BOOK NOOK

BOOK SUGGESTIONS

The Sound of a Wild Snail Eating by Elisabeth Tova Bailey

Snails by Margo Gates (ebook)

The Snail and the Whale by Julia Donaldson

Snippet the Early Riser by Bethanie Murgulia

Snails by Kevin J. Holmes

A Kids Book on Snails by Julie Pearson

Are You a Snail? by Judy Allen

How the Snail Got Her Shell by Danielle Nordahl

Discover Snails by Xist Publishing

The Tale of the Snail Penguin Books Limited

Snail Trail by Ruth Brown

The Snail House by Allan Ahlberg and Gillian Taylor

Wolfsnail: A Backyard Predator by Sarah C. Campbell

The Snail Trail: In Search of a Modern Masterpiece by Jo Saxton

Bees, Snails, & Peacock Tails: Patterns & Shapes by Betsy Franco

The Snail's Spell Book by Joanne Ryder

Snail's Birthday Wish by Fiona Rempt and Noelle Smart

Twelve Snails to One Lizard by Susan Hightower

Common Core Standards Integration

While interacting with students we are rarely aware of the full spectrum of cross-disciplinary standards students are participating in within a lesson or unit of study. When students are constructing a project they will probably be fulfilling several standards depending on the instructors guidance. If students share a written activity orally and ask and answer questions, recount events and even record the event, they are participating in multiple English Language Arts Standards. CCSS.ELA-Literacy includes standards you fulfill when introducing and/or guiding students in projects and answering their questions. (CCSS.ELA-Literacy "Produce complete sentences when appropriate to task and situation....")

When we present a science unit, students may create, experiment, discuss, observe, collect data, record information, illustrate, share, write stories and journals, and they may extend activities beyond the classroom depending on their interest and motivation.

For this unit, to find out if an activity is linked to a Common Core State Standard for your grade level, check the page numbers listed next to the standards.

Although *SNAILOPOLIS* integrates science, language arts, art, math, social studies, and more, the Common Core Standards list is not an exhaustive list. In some cases an entire standard will be listed, but how the instructor presents the standard, and what they require, will determine if the standard is accomplished in its entirety. The standard can be easily fulfilled by asking the questions listed in the standard and/or guiding students in a specific activity or action stated in the standard.

ENGLISH LANGUAGE ARTS STANDARDS – READING: Informational Text

During this unit, students will be listening to and reading texts, writing, and sharing. This category is easily accomplished as you read, share and discuss. Read the statement under Page.

KEY IDEAS and DETAILS	Pages	K	1	2	3/4
CCSS.ELA-Literacy.RI.K.1 With prompting and support, ask and answer questions about key details in a text.		x			
CCSS.ELA-Literacy.RI.K.2 With prompting and support, identify the main topic and retell key details of a text.		x			
CCSS.ELA-Literacy.RI.K.3 With prompting and support, describe the connection between two individuals, events, ideas, or pieces of information in a text.		x			
CCSS.ELA-Literacy.RI.1.1 Ask and answer questions about key details in a text.			x		
CCSS.ELA-Literacy.RI.1.2 Identify the main topic and retell key details of a text.			x		
CCSS.ELA-Literacy.RI.1.3 Describe the connection between two individuals, events, ideas, or pieces of information in a text.			x		
CCSS.ELA-Literacy.RI.(2/3/4).1 Ask and answer such questions as who, what, where, when, why, and how to demonstrate understanding of key details in a text.				x	x
CCSS.ELA-Literacy.RI.(2/3/4).2 Identify the main topic of a multi-paragraph text as well as the focus of specific paragraphs within the text.				x	x
CRAFT and STRUCTURE					
CCSS.ELA-Literacy.RI.K.4 With prompting and support, ask and answer questions about unknown words in a text.		x			
CCSS.ELA-Literacy.RI.K.5 Identify the front cover, back cover, and title page of a book.		x			
CCSS.ELA-Literacy.RI.K.6 Name the author and illustrator of a text and define the role of each in presenting the ideas or information in a text.		x			
CCSS.ELA-Literacy.RI.1.4 Ask and answer questions to help determine or clarify the meaning of words and phrases in a text.			x		
CCSS.ELA-Literacy.RI.1.5 Know and use various text features (e.g., headings, tables of contents, glossaries, electronic menus, icons) to locate key facts or information in a text.			x		
CCSS.ELA-Literacy.RI.1.6 Distinguish between information provided by pictures or other illustrations and information provided by the words in a text.			x		
CCSS.ELA-Literacy.RI.(2/3/4).4 Determine the meaning of words and phrases in a text relevant to a grade 2 topic or subject area.				x	x
CCSS.ELA-Literacy.RI.(2/3/4).5 Know and use various text features (e.g., captions, bold print, subheadings, glossaries, indexes, electronic menus, icons) to locate key facts or information in a text efficiently.				x	x
CCSS.ELA-Literacy.RI.(2/3/4).6 Identify the main purpose of a text, including what the author wants to answer, explain, or describe.				x	x
INTEGRATION of KNOWLEDGE and IDEAS					
CCSS.ELA-Literacy.RI.K.7 With prompting and support, describe the relationship between illustrations and the text in which they appear (e.g., what person, place, thing, or idea in the text an illustration depicts).		x			
CCSS.ELA-Literacy.RI.K.8 With prompting and support, identify the reasons an author gives to support points in a text.		x			
CCSS.ELA-Literacy.RI.K.9 With prompting and support, identify basic similarities in and differences between two texts on the same topic (e.g., in illustrations, descriptions, or procedures).		x			
CCSS.ELA-Literacy.RI.1.7 Use the illustrations and details in a text to describe its key ideas.			x		
CCSS.ELA-Literacy.RI.1.8 Identify the reasons an author gives to support points in a text.			x		
CCSS.ELA-Literacy.RI.(2/3/4).7 Explain how specific images (e.g., a diagram showing how a machine works) contribute to and clarify a text.				x	x
CCSS.ELA-Literacy.RI.(2/3/4).8 Describe how reasons support specific points the author makes in a text.				x	x
CCSS.ELA-Literacy.RI.(2/3/4).9 Compare and contrast the most important points presented by two texts on the same topic.				x	x

The Pages column contains the following vertical text spanning the table: "These standards can be addressed by reading books from the Book Nook, Internet documents, and student writing, and then using the standard descriptions as a guide to ask questions, discuss, prompt, and instruct. Only the standards that can be linked to this unit are included. ENGLISH LANGUAGE ARTS-READING: INFORMATIONAL TEXT"

ENGLISH LANGUAGE ARTS STANDARDS – READING: Foundational Skills

PRINT CONCEPTS	Pages	K	1	2	3/4
CCSS.ELA-Literacy.RF.(K/1).1 Demonstrate understanding of the organization and basic features of print.	ENGLISH LANGUAGE ARTS-READING: Foundational Skills Only the standards that can be linked to this unit are included. These standards can be addressed by reading books from the Book Nook, Internet documents, and student writing, and then using the standard descriptions as a guide to ask questions, discuss, prompt, and instruct.	x	x		
PHONOLOGICAL AWARENESS					
CCSS.ELA-Literacy.RF.(K/1).2 Demonstrate understanding of spoken words, syllables, and sounds (phonemes).		x	x		
PHONICS and WORD RECOGNITION					
CCSS.ELA-Literacy.RF.(K/1/2/3/4).3 Know and apply grade-level phonics and word analysis skills in decoding words.		x	x	x	x
FLUENCY					
CCSS.ELA-Literacy.RF.K.4 Read emergent-reader texts with purpose and understanding.		x			
CCSS.ELA-Literacy.RF.(1/2/3/4).4 Read with sufficient accuracy and fluency to support comprehension.			x	x	x

ENGLISH LANGUAGE ARTS STANDARDS – LANGUAGE

CONVENTIONS of STANDARD ENGLISH	Pages	K	1	2	3/4
CCSS.ELA-Literacy.L.(K/1/2/3/4).1 Demonstrate command of the conventions of standard English grammar and usage when writing or speaking.	Teacher pages, group projects	x	x	x	x
CCSS.ELA-Literacy.L.(K/1/2/3/4).2 Demonstrate command of the conventions of standard English capitalization, punctuation, and spelling when writing.	3, 4, 9, 15, 28-36, 37-40, 41-43, 47-48	x	x	x	x
KNOWLEDGE of LANGUAGE					
CCSS.ELA-Literacy.L.(2/3/4).3 Use knowledge of language and its conventions when writing, speaking, reading, or listening.	Teacher pages, group projects			x	x
VOCABULARY ACQUISITION and USE					
CCSS.ELA-Literacy.L.K.4 Determine or clarify the meaning of unknown and multiple-meaning words and phrases based on kindergarten reading and content.	ENGLISH LANGUAGE ARTS-Language: Vocabulary Acquisition and Use The standards in this section can be accomplished through responses and interactions relating to Teacher Pages, brainstorming and discussing in groups and/or oral presentations, and sharing of written work and projects.	x			
CCSS.ELA-Literacy.L.K.5 With guidance and support from adults, explore word relationships and nuances in word meanings and content.		x			
CCSS.ELA-Literacy.L.K.6 Use words and phrases acquired through conversations, reading and being read to, and responding to texts.		x			
CCSS.ELA-Literacy.L.1.4 and CCSS.ELA-Literacy.L.2.4 Determine or clarify the meaning of unknown and multiple-meaning words and phrases based on grade 1 (grade 2) reading and content, choosing flexibly from an array of strategies.			x	x	
CCSS.ELA-Literacy.L.1.5 With guidance and support from adults, demonstrate understanding of word relationships and nuances in word meanings.			x		
CCSS.ELA-Literacy.L.1.6 Use words and phrases acquired through conversations, reading and being read to, and responding to texts, including using frequently occurring conjunctions to signal simple relationships (e.g., because).			x		
CCSS.ELA-Literacy.L.(2/3/4).5 Demonstrate understanding of word relationships and nuances in word meanings.				x	x
CCSS.ELA-Literacy.L.(2/3/4).6 Use words and phrases acquired through conversations, reading and being read to, and responding to texts, including using adjectives and adverbs to describe.				x	x

ENGLISH LANGUAGE ARTS STANDARDS – WRITING

TEXT TYPES and PURPOSES	Pages	K	1	2	3/4
CCSS.ELA-Literacy.W.K.1 Use a combination of drawing, dictating, and writing to compose opinion pieces in which they tell a reader the (topic) or the name of the book they are writing about and state an opinion or preference about the topic or book (e.g., My favorite book is...).	28-36, 47-48	x			
CCSS.ELA-Literacy.W.K.2 Use a combination of drawing, dictating, and writing to compose informative/explanatory texts in which they name what they are writing about and supply some information about the topic.	26-27, 28-36, 47-48	x			
CCSS.ELA-Literacy.W.K.3 Use a combination of drawing, dictating, and writing to narrate a single event or several loosely linked events, tell about the events in the order in which they occurred, and provide a reaction to what happened.	28-36, 37-40, 41-43, 47-48	x			
CCSS.ELA-Literacy.W.1.1 Write opinion pieces in which they introduce the topic or name the book they are writing about, state an opinion, supply a reason for the opinion, and provide some sense of closure.	28-36, 47-48		x		
CCSS.ELA-Literacy.W.1.2 Write informative/explanatory texts in which they name a topic, supply some facts about the topic, and provide some sense of closure.	26-27, 28-36, 47-48		x		
CCSS.ELA-Literacy.W.(1/2/3/4).3 Write narratives in which they recount two or more appropriately sequenced events, include some details regarding what happened, use temporal words to signal event order, and provide some sense of closure.	28-36, 37-40, 41-43, 47-48		x	x	x
CCSS.ELA-Literacy.W.(2/3/4).1 Write opinion pieces in which they introduce the topic or book they are writing about, state an opinion, supply reasons that support the opinion, use linking words (e.g., because, and, also) to connect opinion and reasons, and provide a concluding statement or section.	28-36, 47-48			x	x
CCSS.ELA-Literacy.W.(2/3/4).2 Write informative/explanatory texts in which they introduce a topic, use facts and definitions to develop points, and provide a concluding statement or section.	28-36, 47-48			x	x
PRODUCTION and DISTRIBUTION of WRITING					
CCSS.ELA-Literacy.W.K.5 With guidance and support from adults, respond to questions and suggestions from peers and add details to strengthen writing as needed.	3, 28-36, 37-40, 41-43, 47-48	x			
CCSS.ELA-Literacy.W.K.6 With guidance and support from adults, explore a variety of digital tools to produce and publish writing, including in collaboration with peers.	28-36	x			
CCSS.ELA-Literacy.W.1.5 With guidance and support from adults, focus on a topic, respond to questions and suggestions from peers, and add details to strengthen writing as needed.	3, 28-36, 37-40, 41-43, 47-48		x		
CCSS.ELA-Literacy.W.(1/2/3/4).6 With guidance and support from adults, use a variety of digital tools to produce and publish writing, including in collaboration with peers.	28-36		x	x	x
CCSS.ELA-Literacy.W.(2/3/4).5 With guidance and support from adults and peers, focus on a topic and strengthen writing as needed by revising and editing.	28-36, 37-40, 41-43, 47-48			x	x
RESEARCH to BUILD and PRESENT KNOWLEDGE					
CCSS.ELA-Literacy.W.K.7 and W.1.7 Participate in shared research and writing projects (e.g., explore a number of books by a favorite author and express opinions about them).	2, 28-36, 37-40, 41-43, 47-48	x	x		
CCSS.ELA-Literacy.W.K.8 and W.1.8 With guidance and support from adults, recall information from experiences or gather information from provided sources to answer a question.	Teacher pages, group projects	x	x		
CCSS.ELA-Literacy.W.(2/3/4).7 Participate in shared research and writing projects (e.g., read a number of books on a single topic to produce a report; record science observations).	4, 24, 28-36, 41-43, 47-48			x	x
CCSS.ELA-Literacy.W.(2/3/4).8 Recall information from experiences or gather information from provided sources to answer a question.	3-4, 6-9, 15, 24, 28-36, 37-40, 41-43, 47-48			x	x

ENGLISH LANGUAGE ARTS STANDARDS – SPEAKING and LISTENING

COMPREHENSION and COLLABORATION	Page	K	1	2	3/4
CCSS.ELA-Literacy.SL.K.1 Participate in collaborative conversations with diverse partners about kindergarten topics and texts with peers and adults in small and larger groups.		x			
CCSS.ELA-Literacy.SL.K.2 Confirm understanding of a text read aloud or information presented orally or through other media by asking and answering questions about key details and requesting clarification if something is not understood.		x			
CCSS.ELA-Literacy.SL.K.3 Ask and answer questions in order to seek help, get information, or clarify something that is not understood.		x			
CCSS.ELA-Literacy.SL.1.1 Participate in collaborative conversations with diverse partners about grade 1 topics and texts with peers and adults in small and larger groups.			x		
CCSS.ELA-Literacy.SL.1.2 Ask and answer questions about key details in a text read aloud or information presented orally or through other media.			x		
CCSS.ELA-Literacy.SL.1.3 Ask and answer questions about what a speaker says in order to gather additional information or clarify something that is not understood.			x		
CCSS.ELA-Literacy.SL.(2/3/4).1 Participate in collaborative conversations with diverse partners about grade (2,3,4) topics and texts with peers and adults in small and larger groups.				x	x
CCSS.ELA-Literacy.SL.(2/3/4).2 Recount or describe key ideas or details from a text read aloud or information presented orally or through other media.				x	x
CCSS.ELA-Literacy.SL.(2/3/4).3 Ask and answer questions about what a speaker says in order to clarify comprehension, gather additional information, or deepen understanding of a topic or issue.				x	x

The standards in this section can be accomplished through responses and interactions relating to Teacher Pages, brainstorming and discussing in groups and/or oral presentations, and sharing of written work and projects.

NOTE: Comprehension and Collaboration
Many activities include books to read, discussion topics and activities that require written and/or hands-on participation. If students are asking questions, discussing the topic and interacting with peers and/or adults, observable comprehension and collaboration standards may be fulfilled. Teachers can expand and elaborate on standard according to time/need.

PRESENTATION of KNOWLEDGE and IDEAS	Page	K	1	2	3/4
CCSS.ELA-Literacy.SL.K.4 Describe familiar people, places, things, and events and, with prompting and support, provide additional detail.	2-3, 24	x			
CCSS.ELA-Literacy.SL.K.5 Add drawings or other visual displays to descriptions as desired to provide additional detail.	3, 20, 24, 26-27, 28-36	x			
CCSS.ELA-Literacy.SL.K.6 Speak audibly and express thoughts, feelings, and ideas clearly.	Teacher pages, group projects, oral presentations	x			
CCSS.ELA-Literacy.SL.1.4 Describe people, places, things, and events with relevant details, expressing ideas and feelings clearly.			x		
CCSS.ELA-Literacy.SL.1.5 Add drawings or other visual displays to descriptions when appropriate to clarify ideas, thoughts, and feelings.	3, 15, 20, 24, 26-27, 28-36		x		
CCSS.ELA-Literacy.SL.1.6 Produce complete sentences when appropriate to task and situation. (See grade 1 Language standards 1 and 3 here for specific expectations.)	Teacher pages, group projects, oral presentations		x		
CCSS.ELA-Literacy.SL.(2/3/4).4 Tell a story or recount an experience with appropriate facts and relevant, descriptive details, speaking audibly in coherent sentences.				x	x
CCSS.ELA-Literacy.SL.(2/3/4).5 Create audio recordings of stories or poems; add drawings or other visual displays to stories or recounts of experiences when appropriate to clarify ideas, thoughts, and feelings.	41-43, oral presentations			x	x
CCSS.ELA-Literacy.SL.(2/3/4).6 Produce complete sentences when appropriate to task and situation in order to provide requested detail or clarification. (See grade 2,3,4 Language standards 1 and 3 here for specific expectations.)	Teacher pages, group projects, oral presentations			x	x

NOTE: Presentation of Knowledge and Ideas
You many cover many more standards than those listed. As students share reports and daata, you can guide them in asking and answering questions. Meeting privately with students is a positive and constructive way to encourage and guide. Audio recordings of stories is a fun and educational tool that helps students hear and critique their own presentations.

SCIENCE STANDARDS
The following activities and science process skills are integrated throughout the unit.

Students will participate in activities to increase science skills:
- inference
- observation
- form a hypothesis
- summarzing
- synthesizing
- collecting data
- recording observations
- identifying and citing evidence to support an idea or position
- analyze/infer causes/effects
- evaluate
- determine the main idea
- diagram
- organize data

SCIENCE PROGRESS STRATEGIES
- Students read and write about science topics.
- Students use graphic organizers to "show" science.
- Students discuss science vocabulary and illustrations.
- Students write science learning reports.
- Students make and interpret data tables and graphs.

MATH STANDARDS

COUNTING and CARDINALITY	Page	K	1	2	3/4
• Know number names and the count sequence • Count to tell the number of objects • Compare numbers	14, 26	x			
OPERATIONS and ALGEBRAIC THINKING					
• Understand addition as putting together and adding to, and understand subtraction as taking apart and taking from.	14	x			
• Represent and solve problems involving addition and subtraction. • Understand and apply properties of operations and the relationship between addition and subtraction. • Add and subtract within 20. • Work with addition and subtraction equations.	18		x		
• Represent and solve problems involving addition and subtraction. • Add and subtract within 20. • Work with equal groups of objects to gain foundations for multiplication.	18			x	
• Represent and solve problems involving multiplication and division. • Understand properties of multiplication and the relationship between multiplication and division. • Multiply and divide within 100. • Solve problems involving the four operations, and identify and explain patterns in arithmetic.	18				x
NUMBER and OPERATIONS in BASE 10					
• Extend the counting sequence. • Understand place value. • Use place value understanding and properties of operations to add and subtract.	14-15, 18		x	x	
• Generalize place value understanding for multi-digit whole numbers. • Use place value understanding and properties of operations to perform multi-digit arithmetic.	18				x
MEASUREMENT DATA					
• Describe and compare measurable attributes. • Classify objects and count the number of objects in categories.	14, 26	x			
• Measure lengths indirectly and by iterating length units. • Tell and write time. • Represent and interpret data.	14-15, 18		x		
• Measure and estimate lengths in standard units. • Relate addition and subtraction to length. • Work with time and money. • Represent and interpret data.	14-15, 18			x	
• Solve problems involving measurement and conversion of measurements from a larger unit to a smaller unit. • Represent and interpret data.	15, 18				x
GEOMETRY					
• Identify and describe shapes. • Analyze, compare, create, and compose shapes.	26	x			
• Reason with shapes and their attributes.	26		x	x	x
• Draw and identify lines and angles, and classify shapes by properties of their lines and angles.	26				x

MATHEMATICAL PRACTICES

1. Make sense of problems and persevere in solving them.
2. Reason abstractly and quantitatively.
3. Construct viable arguments and critique the reasoning of others.
4. Model with mathematics.
5. Use appropriate tools strategically.
6. Attend to precision.
7. Look for and make use of structure.
8. Look for and express regularity in repeated reasoning.